PYTHAGORAS EDITION

DESTROY THIS BOOK
in the name of
MATHS!

Buster Books

WRITTEN, DRAWN AND CREATED BY
MIKE BARFIELD

EDITED BY LAUREN FARNSWORTH
DESIGNED BY ZOE BRADLEY
COVER DESIGN BY ANGIE ALLISON
CONSULTANCY BY DAVID GLOVER

WITH A LITTLE HELP FROM THESE GENIUSES ...

PYTHAGORAS | ALAN TURING | KATHERINE JOHNSON

AND NOT FORGETTING THESE FIGURES TOO ...

MIKE BARFIELD | A TURTLE | YOU

First published in Great Britain in 2018 by Buster Books, an imprint of
Michael O'Mara Books Limited, 9 Lion Yard, Tremadoc Road, London SW4 7NQ

 www.busterbooks.co.uk   Buster Children's Books   @BusterBooks

Copyright © Mike Barfield 2018

Layout copyright © Buster Books 2018

A CIP catalogue record for this book is available from the British Library.

ISBN: 978-1-78055-530-0

1 3 5 7 9 10 8 6 4 2

This book was printed in April 2018 by Leo Paper Products Ltd,
Heshan Astros Printing Limited, Xuantan Temple Industrial Zone,
Gulao Town, Heshan City, Guangdong Province, China.

CONTENTS

ABOUT THE AUTHOR

Mike Barfield is a writer, cartoonist, poet and performer. He has worked in TV and radio, as well as in schools, libraries, museums and bookshops, and has a first-class science degree.

INTRODUCTION

This book is calculated to keep you entertained for hours. Packed into its pages you will find lots of projects to press out, and even more to cut out, stick, fold, colour in and doodle on.

Your mission is to **DESTROY** this book by making all of its marvellous mathematical models, attempting the many perplexing puzzles, and having tons of fun in the process. There are bite-sized facts to snack on too, and numerous nuggets of mind-boggling number-based knowledge.

You don't need any expensive or hard-to-find craft supplies to complete the projects. Most of the models can be built with glue and sticky tape. You can also use pens and pencils to make the designs look the way you want and to colour them in. Just run and grab these simple weapons of maths destruction ...

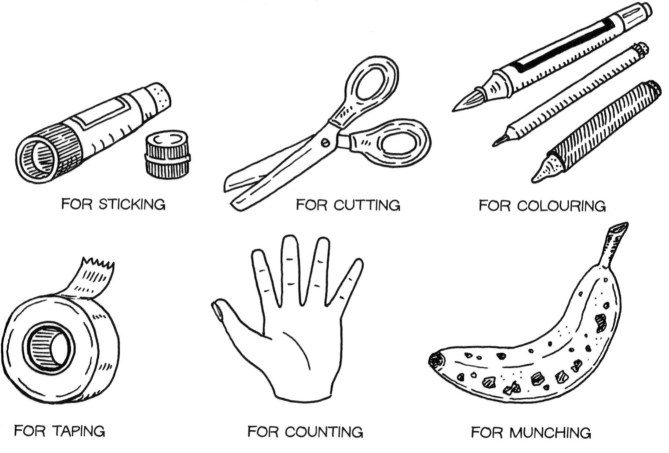

FOR STICKING   FOR CUTTING   FOR COLOURING

FOR TAPING   FOR COUNTING   FOR MUNCHING

 NOW, LET THE DESTRUCTION BEGIN!

THINK OF A NUMBER

USE THESE CARDS TO READ MINDS MATHEMAGICALLY!

Card 1:

1	3	5	7
9	11	13	15
17	19	21	23
25	27	29	31
33	35	37	39
41	43	45	47
49	51	53	55
57	59	☆	☆

Card 2:

2	3	6	7
10	11	14	15
18	19	22	23
26	27	30	31
34	35	38	39
42	43	46	47
50	51	54	55
58	59	☆	☆

Card 3:

4	5	6	7
12	13	14	15
20	21	22	23
28	29	30	31
36	37	38	39
44	45	46	47
52	53	54	55
60	☆	☆	☆

Card 4:

8	9	10	11
12	13	14	15
24	25	26	27
28	29	30	31
40	41	42	43
44	45	46	47
56	57	58	59
60	☆	☆	☆

Card 5:

16	17	18	19
20	21	22	23
24	25	26	27
28	29	30	31
48	49	50	51
52	53	54	55
56	57	58	59
60	☆	☆	☆

Card 6:

32	33	34	35
36	37	38	39
40	41	42	43
44	45	46	47
48	49	50	51
52	53	54	55
56	57	58	59
60	☆	☆	☆

☆ WHAT YOU DO

Carefully cut out the six cards with scissors.

Tell a friend you will read their mind using the 'magic of maths'. Ask them to think of a number from 1 to 60. Next, hand them all 6 cards and ask them to give back every card that has their secret number on it. Now comes the magic!

NEXT

Concentrate and pretend you are reading their mind. Instead, sneakily add up the numbers in the top-left corner of each card you have been handed back. The total will give you the number they chose. WOW!

WHAT'S THE MATHS?

The cards use the binary, or 'base 2', system of numbers. Instead of 'units, tens, hundreds' and so on, binary has 'units, twos, fours, eights, sixteens, thirty-twos' and so on. Each '1 – 60' number appears on a card according to how it can be broken down in binary. For example, the number **15 = 1 + 2 + 4 + 8** *– so* **15** *appears on those four cards only. Maths magic!*

MATHS ISLAND

Back in 1852, British mathematician Francis Guthrie (1831 – 1899) suggested only four colours were needed to fill in any map so that no neighbouring ('adjacent') areas were the same colour. He was right – but it took until 1976, and a computer, to prove. It is now known as 'The Four-Colour Theorem'. Can you colour 'Maths Island' using the same rules and no more than four colours?

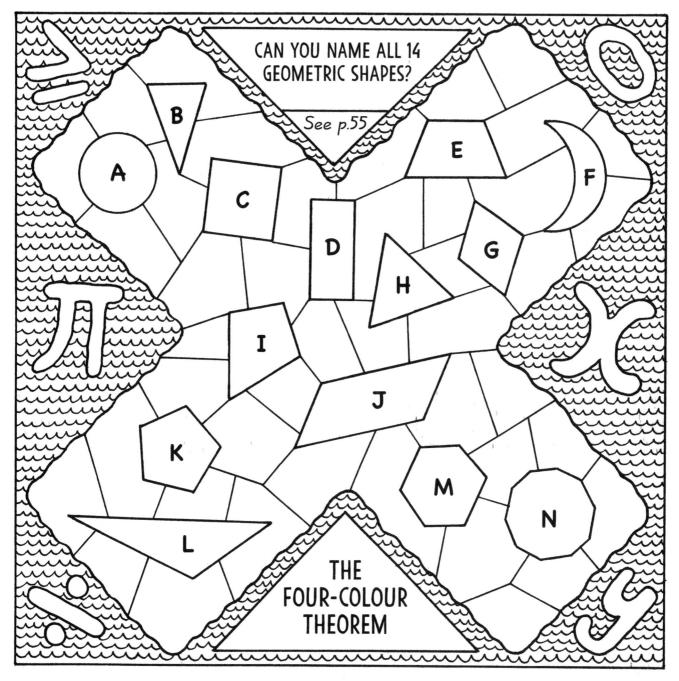

CAN YOU NAME ALL 14 GEOMETRIC SHAPES?

See p.55

THE FOUR-COLOUR THEOREM

BUST OF PYTHAGORAS IN
THE VATICAN MUSEUM

Pythagoras is the most famous maths teacher ever, with his own secretive school of dedicated followers. Born on the Greek island of Samos in about 570 BCE, he has a famous theorem named after him. It concerns the hypotenuse ("hi-pot-en-yoos") of a right-angled triangle – which is the longest side of a right-angled triangle, opposite its right angle.

Pythagoras' Theorem states that the area of the square on the hypotenuse of a right-angled triangle is equal in area to the sum of the squares of the other two sides.

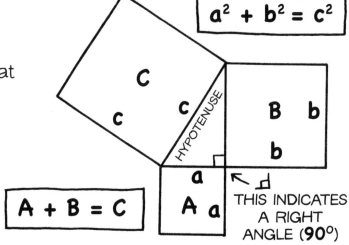

$$a^2 + b^2 = c^2$$

$$A + B = C$$

THIS INDICATES A RIGHT ANGLE (**90°**)

ALTHOUGH THE THEOREM BEARS HIS NAME, THE PRINCIPLE WAS ALREADY KNOWN 1,000 YEARS EARLIER.

Pythagoras had a big golden birthmark on one leg – some claimed it was a sign that he was super special!

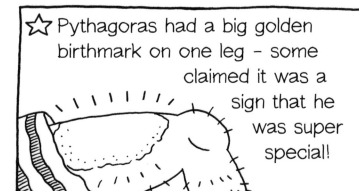

FAB FACT:

Pythagoras' pupils were not allowed foods that might give them wind.

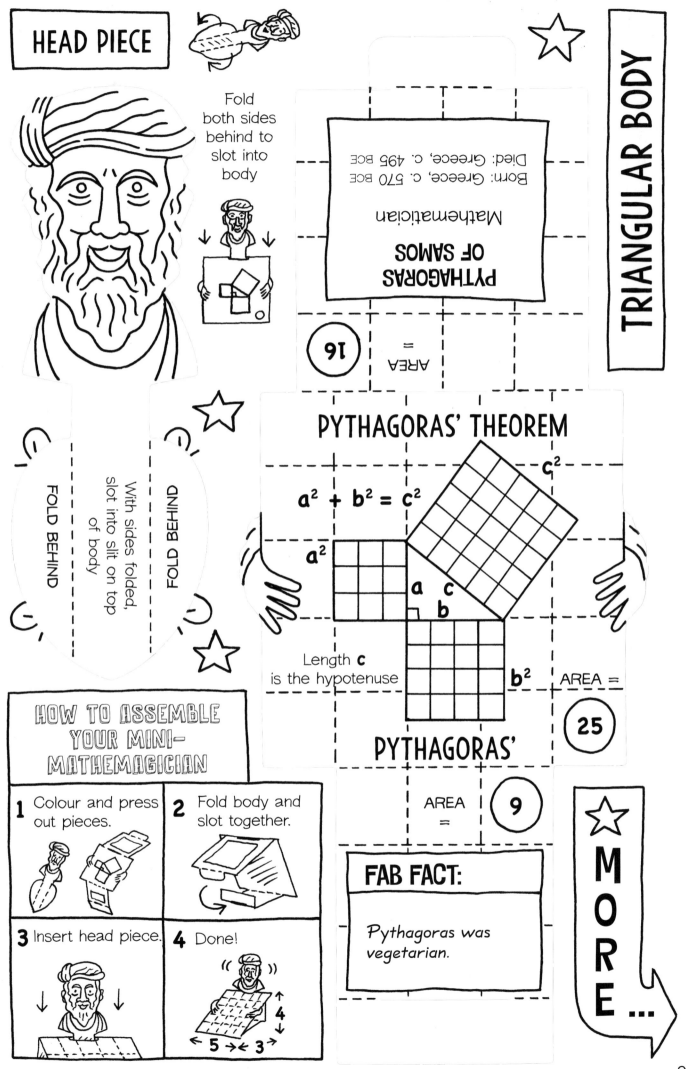

HEAD PIECE

Fold both sides behind to slot into body

TRIANGULAR BODY

PYTHAGORAS OF SAMOS

Mathematician

Born: Greece, c. 570 BCE
Died: Greece, c. 495 BCE

16

AREA =

FOLD BEHIND

With sides folded, slot into slit on top of body

FOLD BEHIND

PYTHAGORAS' THEOREM

$a^2 + b^2 = c^2$

c^2

a^2

a c
b

Length **c** is the hypotenuse

b^2

AREA =

25

PYTHAGORAS'

AREA =

9

HOW TO ASSEMBLE YOUR MINI-MATHEMAGICIAN

1 Colour and press out pieces.

2 Fold body and slot together.

3 Insert head piece.

4 Done!

5   3

4

FAB FACT:

Pythagoras was vegetarian.

MORE ...

There are lots of proofs for Pythagoras' Theorem, including the below.

You can cut it up to show the two smaller squares equal the area of the larger one.

I TOLD YOU!

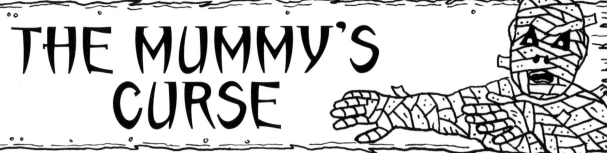

THE MUMMY'S CURSE

⭐ The wrapped remains of ancient Egyptian king Tutankhamun have set you a fiendish task. Colour the pieces below, press them out and glue them to form two identical shapes. It seems simple, but can you then combine them to form a pyramid?

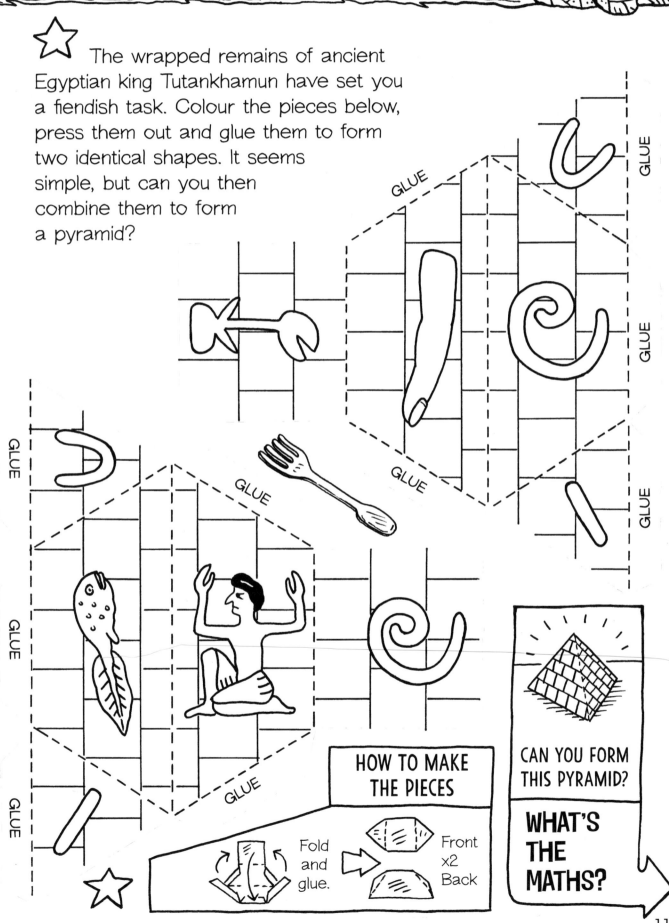

HOW TO MAKE THE PIECES

Fold and glue.

Front x2 Back

CAN YOU FORM THIS PYRAMID?

WHAT'S THE MATHS?

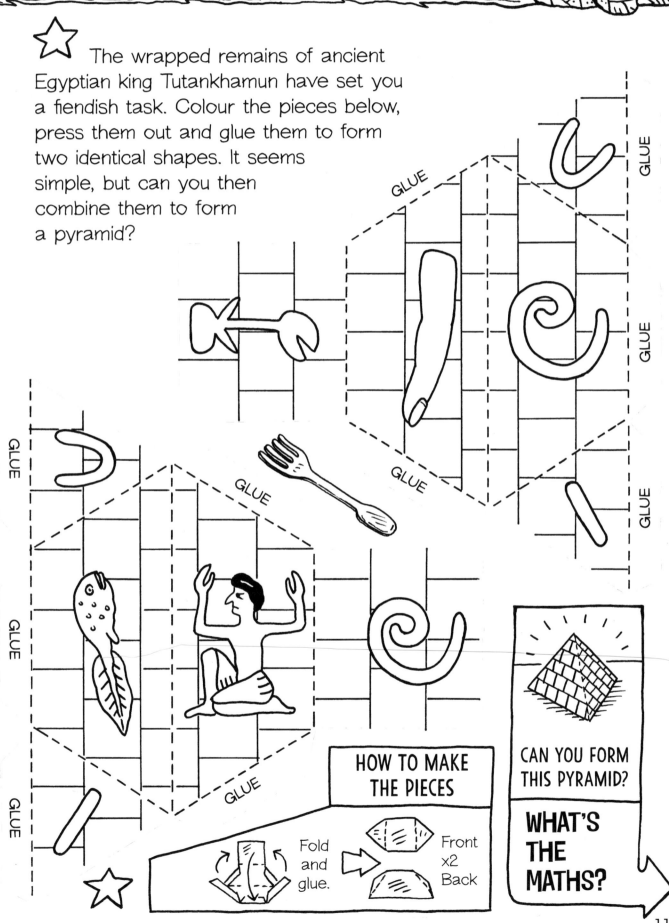

☆ The triangle-based pyramid you can make is a regular tetrahedron ('four-sided form') and is the first of what mathematicians call the five 'Platonic Solids'. The Platonic Solids each have identical faces with identical corner angles and equal length sides. For this tetrahedral pyramid, the faces are all equilateral triangles.
An equilateral triangle has sides and angles that are all the same.

60°
60° 60°

EQUILATERAL
TRIANGLE

☆ Platonic solids were named after the Greek philosopher Plato.

(c. 428 BCE – c. 348 BCE)

PLATO

☆ Ancient Egyptians used pictures ('hieroglyphs') for their numbers.

𝖨	∩	𝒞	𝄐			🧍
1	10	100	1,000	10,000	100,000	1,000,000

☆ Using the key above, can you total up all the numbers on both pieces?

See the answer on page 55.

SHAPE SHIFTER

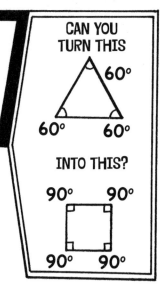

CAN YOU TURN THIS

60°

60°   60°

INTO THIS?

90°   90°

90°   90°

Colour and then carefully press out the shapes below, not forgetting to colour both sides. Then, ignoring the circular holes on some corners, can you put the pieces together to form first an equilateral triangle and then a square of the same area?

(Going mad? See the answer on page 55.)

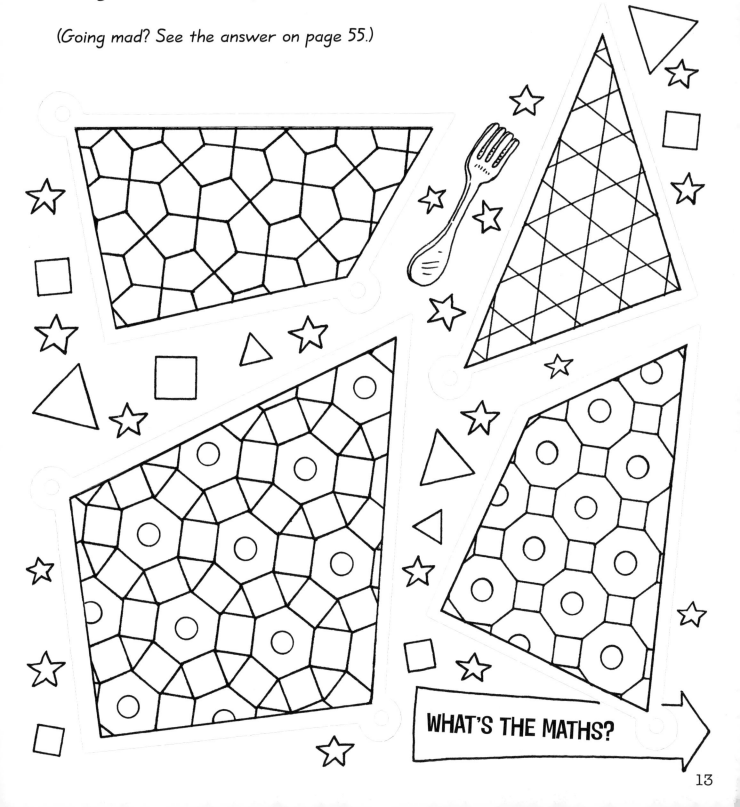

WHAT'S THE MATHS?

13

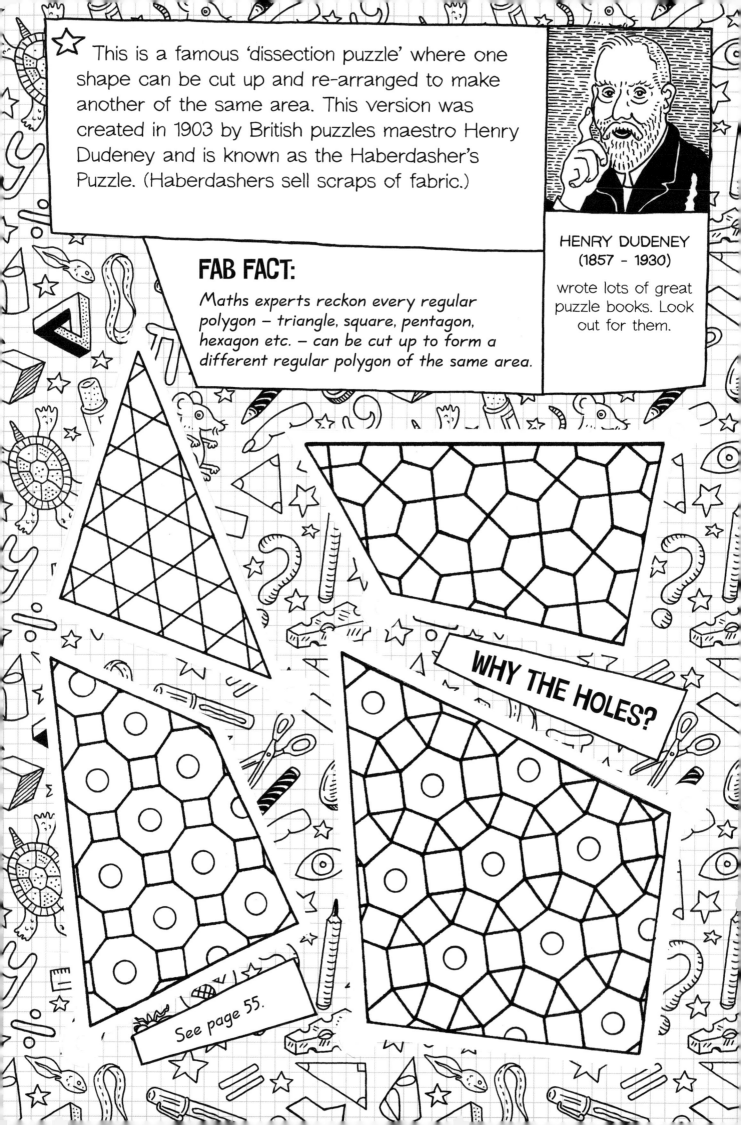

☆ This is a famous 'dissection puzzle' where one shape can be cut up and re-arranged to make another of the same area. This version was created in 1903 by British puzzles maestro Henry Dudeney and is known as the Haberdasher's Puzzle. (Haberdashers sell scraps of fabric.)

HENRY DUDENEY
(1857 - 1930)

wrote lots of great puzzle books. Look out for them.

FAB FACT:

Maths experts reckon every regular polygon – triangle, square, pentagon, hexagon etc. – can be cut up to form a different regular polygon of the same area.

WHY THE HOLES?

See page 55.

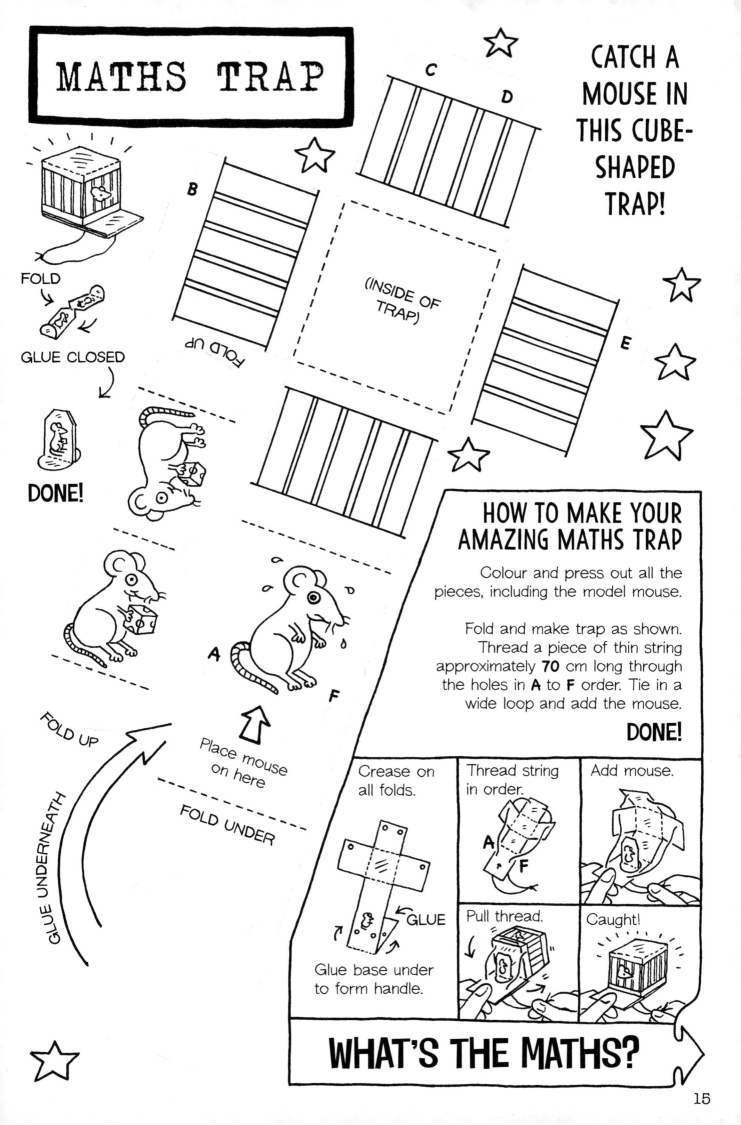

MATHS TRAP

FOLD

GLUE CLOSED

DONE!

B

C

D

(INSIDE OF TRAP)

FOLD UP

E

FOLD UP

GLUE UNDERNEATH

Place mouse on here

FOLD UNDER

A

F

HOW TO MAKE YOUR AMAZING MATHS TRAP

Colour and press out all the pieces, including the model mouse.

Fold and make trap as shown. Thread a piece of thin string approximately **70** cm long through the holes in **A** to **F** order. Tie in a wide loop and add the mouse.

DONE!

Crease on all folds.

Glue base under to form handle.

GLUE

Thread string in order.

A

F

Add mouse.

Pull thread.

Caught!

WHAT'S THE MATHS?

15

Ignoring the handle, the trap forms a cube.

Cubes have six square faces.

A cube is known technically as a hexahedron. It is the second of the five Platonic solids.

Me again!

PLATO

Can you see a cube?

In maths, a flat plan that can be folded up to form a solid is called a 'net'. A cube has eleven possible nets. Of the twelve nets below, which one will NOT give you a cube when folded?

Fold and glue to base to form handle.

A 'NET' OF A CUBE

A B C D E

F G H I

J K L

Answer on page 55.

CREASE ME UP

☆ CREATE AN AMAZING MATHEMATICAL CURVE JUST BY REPEATEDLY FOLDING THIS PAGE.

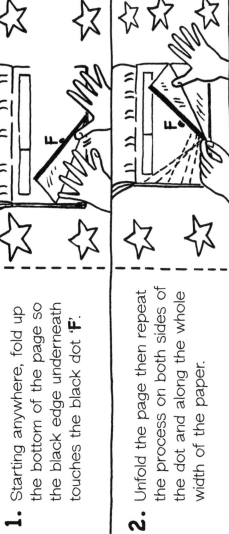

1. Starting anywhere, fold up the bottom of the page so the black edge underneath touches the black dot 'F'.

2. Unfold the page then repeat the process on both sides of the dot and along the whole width of the paper.

3. As if by magic, a curve should begin to appear on the page.

F ●

WHAT'S THE MATHS?

IT'S CR-EASY

The curve created by the creases is called a 'parabola' ("pah-rab-o-la"). The black dot **'F'** is its focus and the horizontal edge of the page used to generate the parabola is known to mathematicians as the directrix.

If you spin a parabola through 360 degrees you get a bowl-shape called a 'paraboloid'.

Paraboloids have lots of uses. The light reflector in a torch is a paraboloid, as is the dish of a satellite TV aerial.

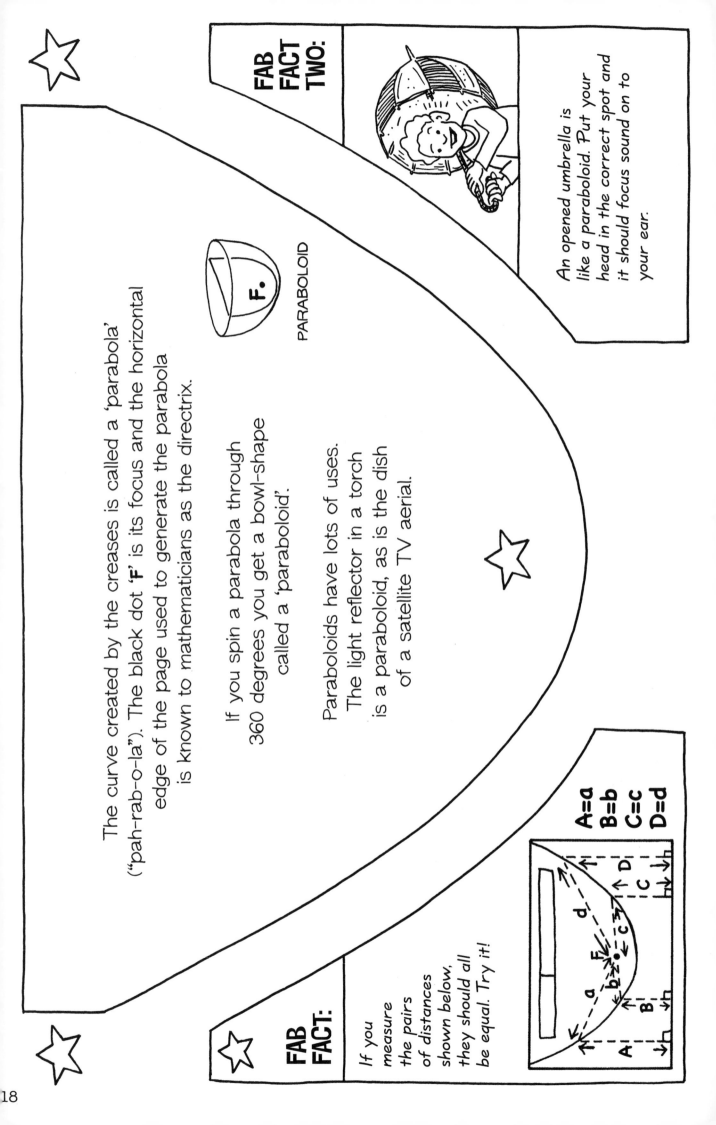

PARABOLOID

FAB FACT TWO:

An opened umbrella is like a paraboloid. Put your head in the correct spot and it should focus sound on to your ear.

FAB FACT:

If you measure the pairs of distances shown below, they should all be equal. Try it!

A=a
B=b
C=c
D=d

TOTAL THAT TURTLE

MAKE A MODEL TURTLE THAT ADDS UP LIKE MAGIC IN EVERY DIRECTION.

An old Chinese legend tells of a turtle that crawls out of a river in front of an emperor. The emperor notices that its shell bears a **3 x 3** pattern of plates, each with a different number of dots, from **1** to **9**. Amazingly, when he adds up the dots in a line horizontally, vertically or diagonally he always gets the same total.

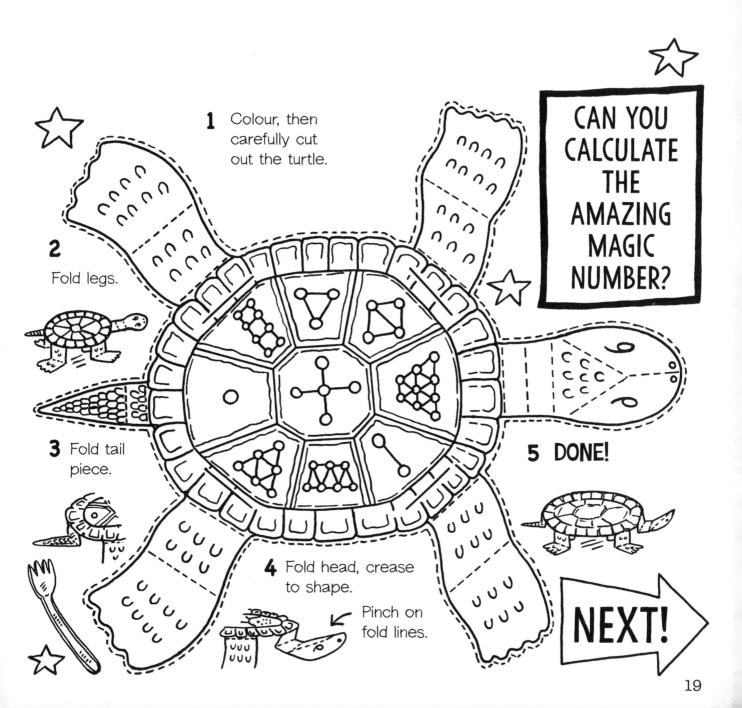

1 Colour, then carefully cut out the turtle.

2 Fold legs.

3 Fold tail piece.

4 Fold head, crease to shape.

Pinch on fold lines.

5 DONE!

CAN YOU CALCULATE THE AMAZING MAGIC NUMBER?

NEXT!

19

WHAT'S THE MATHS?

The turtle's shell is a form of 'magic square' – a numerical grid where the numbers produce the same total in all directions along a straight line. Magic!

9		25		11
	21		12	
22		13		4
	14		5	
15		1		17

CAN YOU SOLVE AND COMPLETE THESE MAGIC SQUARES?

	3	4
1	5	
6		2

1	14		11
	4	10	
12		13	
6	9	3	16

See page 55 for help.

Cut out the completed squares and you can fit them into the slots in the shell.

The Chinese call this magic square the 'Lo Shu' and some believe it has special mystical powers.

CUT
SLOT

CUT
SLOT

CUT
SLOT

CUT
SLOT

A 'Lo Shu' square totals **15** on its lines.

4	9	2
3	5	7
8	1	6

SLOT INTO SHELL

1 Carefully colour, cut-out, fold and glue together your amazing tell-o-scope.

Glue triangles together and then form a square viewing tube.

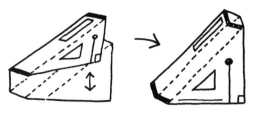

TELL-O-SCOPE

CALCULATE HEIGHTS WITH THIS MINI-MARVEL.

2 Pierce hole in the handle (carefully!) and insert some thin thread.

Pierce hole.

Insert thread, tie in wide loop.

Add sticky-tack or other small weight.

DONE!

3 Measure your height to eye level and also your stride length, as shown on the left.

EYES	STRIDE LENGTH

Note them down.

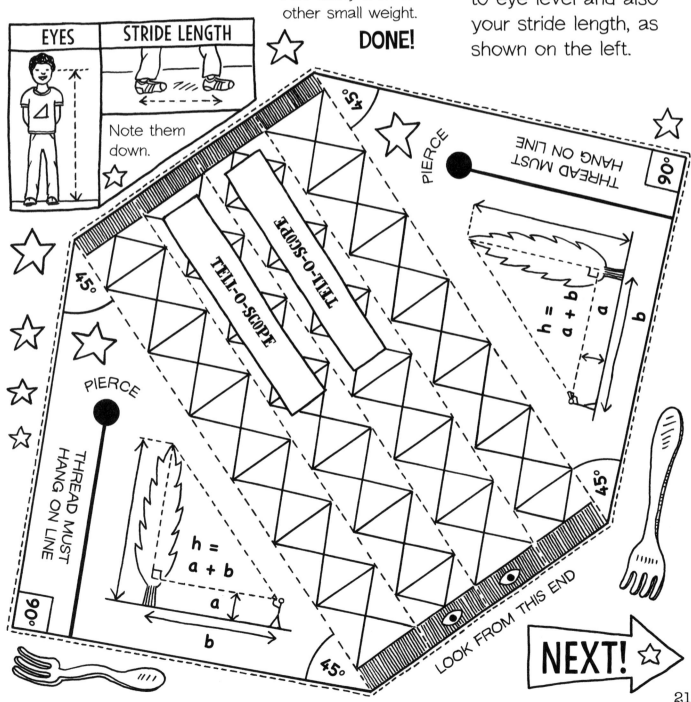

PIERCE

THREAD MUST HANG ON LINE

45°

90°

$h = a + b$

a

b

LOOK FROM THIS END

NEXT!

21

HOW TO USE YOUR TELL-O-SCOPE

⭐ To find the height of a tall object, stand where you can view its summit through your Tell-O-Scope with the thread hanging vertically over the line.

Now count the number of strides you are away from the object.

The object's height (**h**) is given by the formula: **h = a + b**

a = the height of your eye from the ground (in metres)

b = number of strides to object × stride length (in metres)

WHAT'S THE MATHS?

⭐ Your tell-o-scope is a 45°/ 45°/ 90° triangle. This triangle has two sides of the same length.

⭐ When you correctly view your object, you are creating a giant invisible 45°/ 45°/ 90° right-angled triangle – plus your own height.

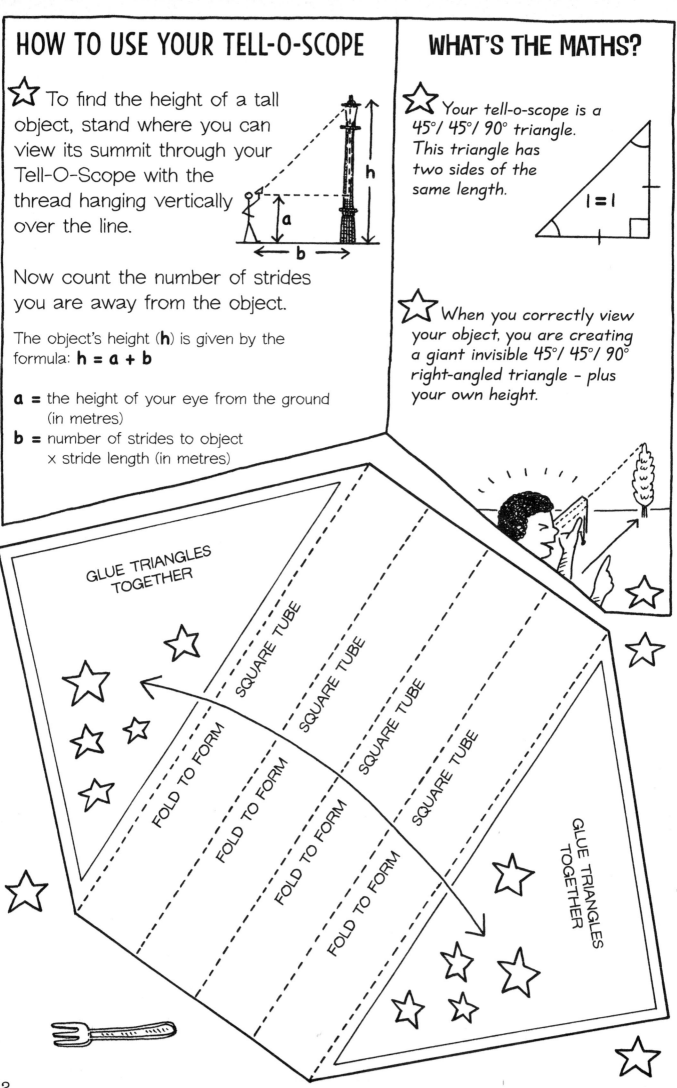

GLUE TRIANGLES TOGETHER

SQUARE TUBE

SQUARE TUBE

SQUARE TUBE

SQUARE TUBE

SQUARE TUBE

FOLD TO FORM

FOLD TO FORM

FOLD TO FORM

FOLD TO FORM

FOLD TO FORM

GLUE TRIANGLES TOGETHER

FACE INVADERS

CAN YOU HELP SAVE PLANET EARTH?

☆ Help! Earth is under attack from 64 evil emojibots. Only YOU can neutralize the threat by placing eight coins on their attack formation so that no two or more coins are in the same line vertically, horizontally or diagonally. Can you save Earth in under 5 minutes? ☆

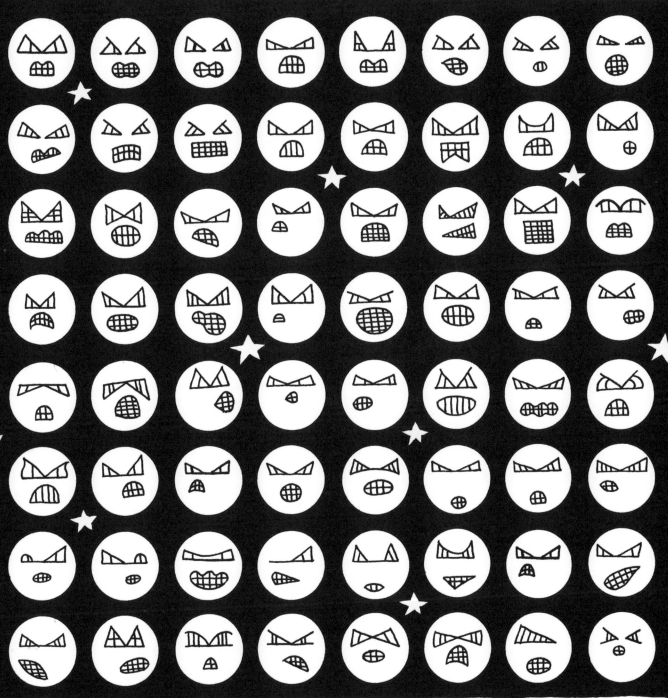

☆ **LOSING THE BATTLE?** *Check out the answer on page 55.*
ONCE YOU'VE WON, COLOUR THE PICTURE. ☆

MAKE YOUR OWN MATHEMAGICIAN
NO. 2: ROGER PENROSE

SIR ROGER

British brainiac Sir Roger Penrose (born 1931) is one of the greatest names in modern maths. He used maths to explore black holes in space, the Big Bang, and even human consciousness.

As well as mind-boggling maths, Sir Roger has a famous optical illusion named after him: 'The Penrose Triangle'. He called it, "impossibility in its purest form" – but you can make one using this book.

Sir Roger also came up with two shapes that now bear his name. These combine to give tiled patterns that never repeat!

YOU CAN CREATE YOUR OWN PENROSE TILINGS USING THE STENCILS ON THE NEXT PAGE.

PENROSE 'KITE'

PENROSE 'DART'

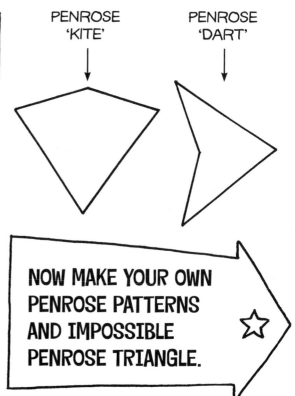

NOW MAKE YOUR OWN PENROSE PATTERNS AND IMPOSSIBLE PENROSE TRIANGLE.

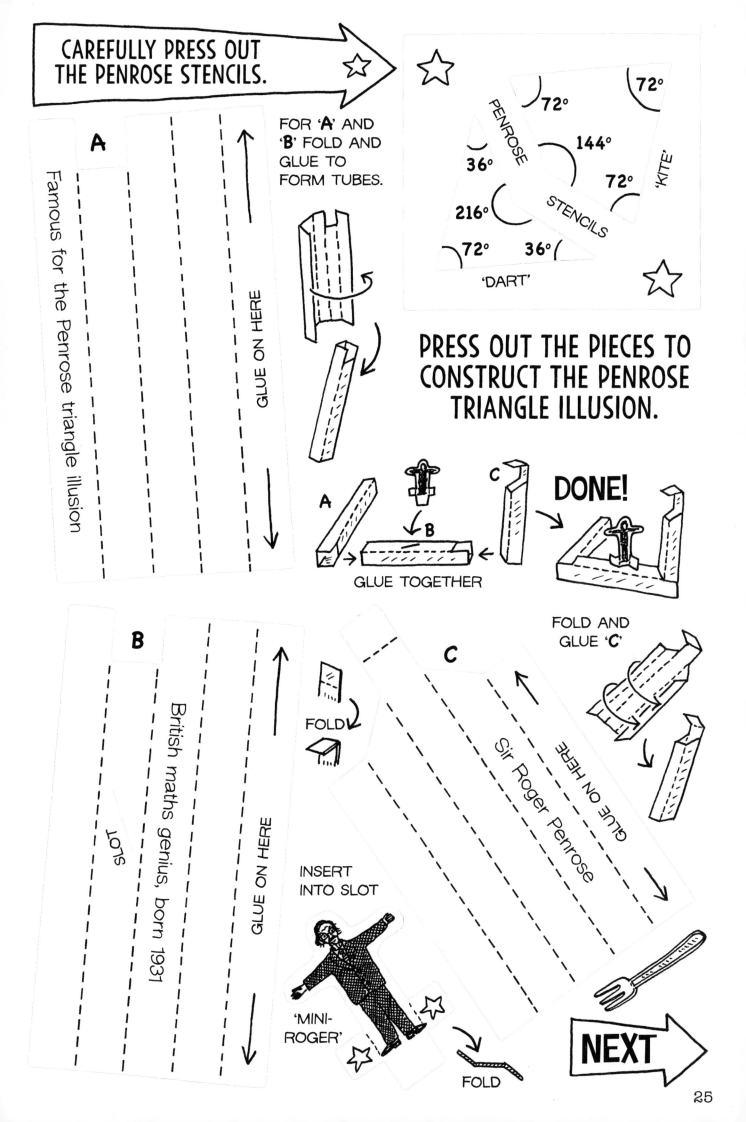

CAREFULLY PRESS OUT THE PENROSE STENCILS.

A

Famous for the Penrose triangle illusion

GLUE ON HERE

FOR 'A' AND 'B' FOLD AND GLUE TO FORM TUBES.

PENROSE 72° 72°

144° 'KITE'

36° 72°

STENCILS

216°

72° 36°

'DART'

PRESS OUT THE PIECES TO CONSTRUCT THE PENROSE TRIANGLE ILLUSION.

A

B

C

GLUE TOGETHER

DONE!

FOLD AND GLUE 'C'

B

British maths genius, born 1931

GLUE ON HERE

SLOT

FOLD

C

Sir Roger Penrose

GLUE ON HERE

INSERT INTO SLOT

'MINI-ROGER'

FOLD

NEXT

25

Match up the sides.

'KITE'

'DART'

Can you fill a whole page with these shapes?

Draw against the edges like a stencil.

HOW TO USE YOUR PENROSE STENCILS

Draw on to paper through the gaps

View your Penrose Triangle model from an angle with one eye closed ... Wow!

ROGER PENROSE

⭐ The octahedron is the third of the five Platonic solids.

⭐ It has eight faces, each of them an equilateral triangle.

EQUILATERAL TRIANGLE
60° 60° 60°

⭐ Colour the model, press it out, crease on all the folds then simply glue each tab under its adjacent edge.

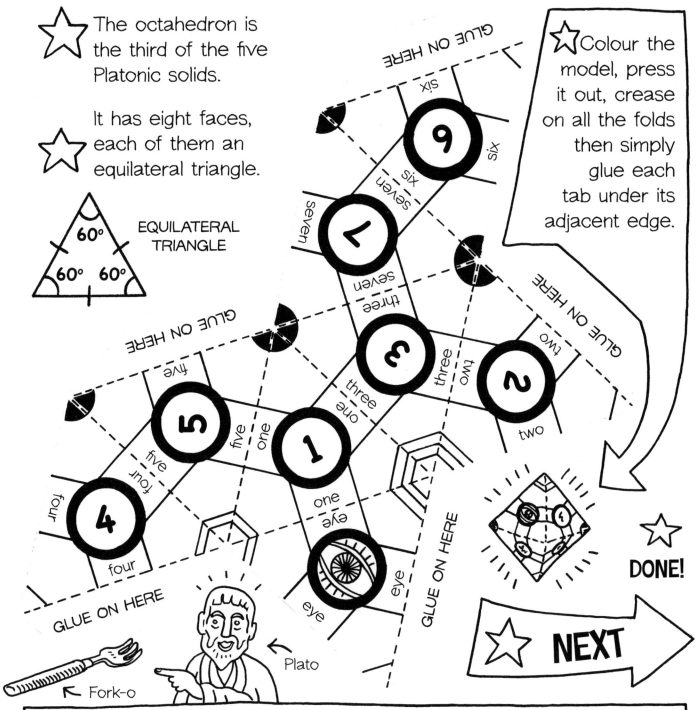

GLUE ON HERE

9 six six seven

7 seven seven three

3 three three two one one

2 two two

5 five five one

1 one eye eye

4 four four four

GLUE ON HERE

GLUE ON HERE

GLUE ON HERE

DONE!

⭐ NEXT

← Fork-o

← Plato

FAB FACT: The parts of a solid have special names.

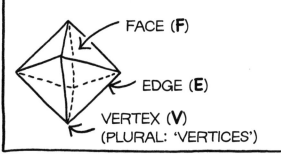

FACE (**F**)

EDGE (**E**)

VERTEX (**V**)
(PLURAL: 'VERTICES')

For all 5 Platonic solids
F + V − E = 2
where **F** = the number of faces;
V = the number of vertices; and
E = the number of edges.

HOW TO USE YOUR ALL-SEEING OCTAHEDRON

1 Ask a friend to think of a number from 1 to 7.

2 Hold the model so the single-lined vertex faces you and your friend can see the other side.

3 Ask your friend if they can see their number. If they say 'Yes' score '1' in your head. A 'No' scores zero.

YOU SEE	THEY SEE
2 6 4	1 3 7 5

4 Now repeat the question with the double-lined vertex facing you.

THEY SEE

2 6 3 7

Score '2' for a 'Yes', zero for a 'No'.

5 Finally, repeat with the three-lined vertex.

YOU SEE	THEY SEE
3 1 2	7 6 5 4

This time score '4' for a 'Yes' and '0' for a 'No'.

AND NOW FOR THE MAGIC.

6 Add up all three scores in your head. The total will be your friend's number.

WHAT'S THE MATHS?

Once again, this trick is based on binary numbers - a system of counting in 1s, 2s, 4s, 8s and so on, rather than in base 10 (units, tens, hundreds, etc.).

ALL IN ORDER

☆ Colour and press out these punched and slotted cards. Each shows a pioneer in the history of computing. Put them in a pile, shuffle them up, then grab a pencil and follow the instructions over the page to put them in date order as if by magic.

NEXT! ☆

TIM BERNERS-LEE

(BORN 1955)

British inventor of the World Wide Web and of the first ever web browser.

HOW TO SORT YOUR MAGIC CARDS

1 With the portraits facing you, insert a pencil into the left-hand holes.

2 Lift up 'hooked' cards and place in front of pack.

3 Repeat the process for the next two holes.

4 The cards will now be in order.

WHAT'S THE MATHS?

It's binary numbers again. The holes and slots represent the decimal numbers '0' to '6' in order.

CHARLES BABBAGE

(1791 - 1871)

English genius who came up with the idea of the digital programmable computer.

JOSEPH MARIE JACQUARD

(1752 - 1834)

French weaver who first used punched cards to control his looms.

BLAISE PASCAL

(1623 - 1662)

French maths prodigy who devised the first ever mechanical calculator.

ALAN TURING

(1912 - 1954)

British boffin considered by many to be the 'father of computer science'.

HERMAN HOLLERITH

(1860 - 1929)

American inventor of the first punched card machine for recording data.

ADA LOVELACE

(1815 - 1852)

Friend of Babbage, Ada wrote the first ever computer program.

THE MAGIC DODECAHEDRON

MAKE THIS AMAZING 12-SIDED SOLID, THEN TRY AND FIND THE MISSING MAGIC NUMBERS.

Colour the net, press it out, and crease all the folds in advance. Then form the model into a ball by gluing the tabs under adjacent faces so that the numbers on the corners (vertices) match.

LIKE THIS! →

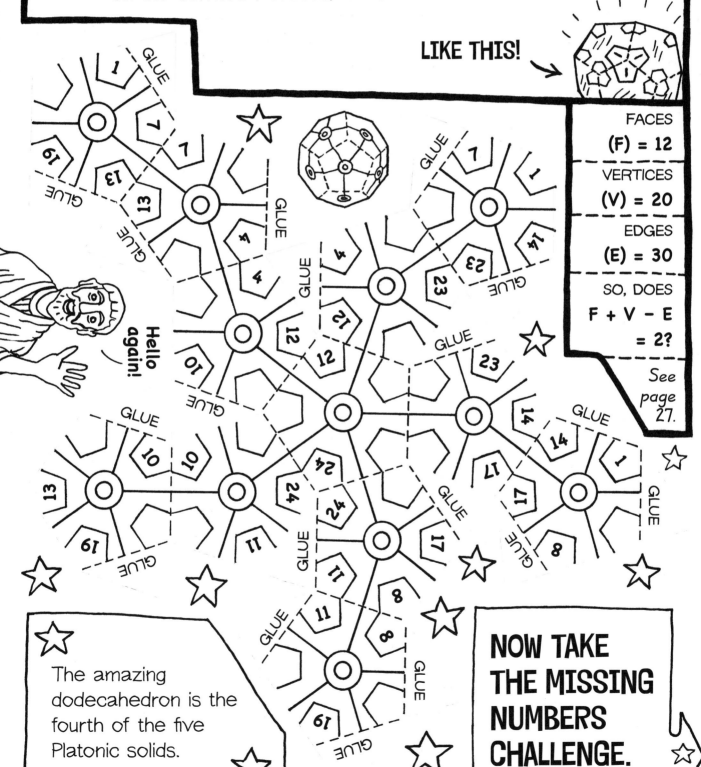

FACES
(F) = 12
VERTICES
(V) = 20
EDGES
(E) = 30
SO, DOES
F + V − E
= 2?

See page 27.

Hello again!

The amazing dodecahedron is the fourth of the five Platonic solids.

NOW TAKE THE MISSING NUMBERS CHALLENGE.

The dodecahedron you create on page 31 is magic. Each of its twelve faces is like a line in a magic square (see page 20). Place the correct five numbers in the corners of each face and they will all add up to the same total. Can you work out the magic total, and then fill in the missing numbers?

$$A + B + C + D + E = ?$$

If you need some clues the magic total and missing numbers are both shown below.

NEED A TIP?
See page 55.

The missing numbers are 2, 5, 6, 18, 20, 21 and 25.

The numbers for each face should all add up to:
65

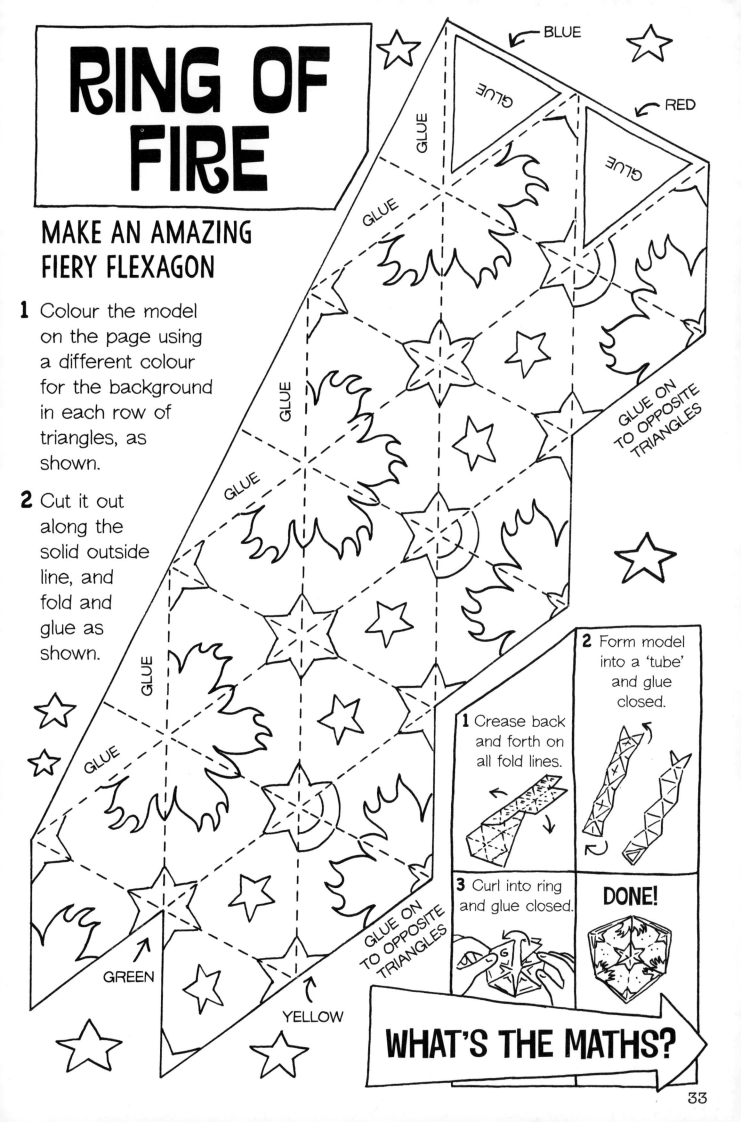

RING OF FIRE

MAKE AN AMAZING FIERY FLEXAGON

1 Colour the model on the page using a different colour for the background in each row of triangles, as shown.

2 Cut it out along the solid outside line, and fold and glue as shown.

GLUE ON TO OPPOSITE TRIANGLES

GLUE ON TO OPPOSITE TRIANGLES

BLUE

RED

GREEN

YELLOW

1 Crease back and forth on all fold lines.

2 Form model into a 'tube' and glue closed.

3 Curl into ring and glue closed.

DONE!

WHAT'S THE MATHS?

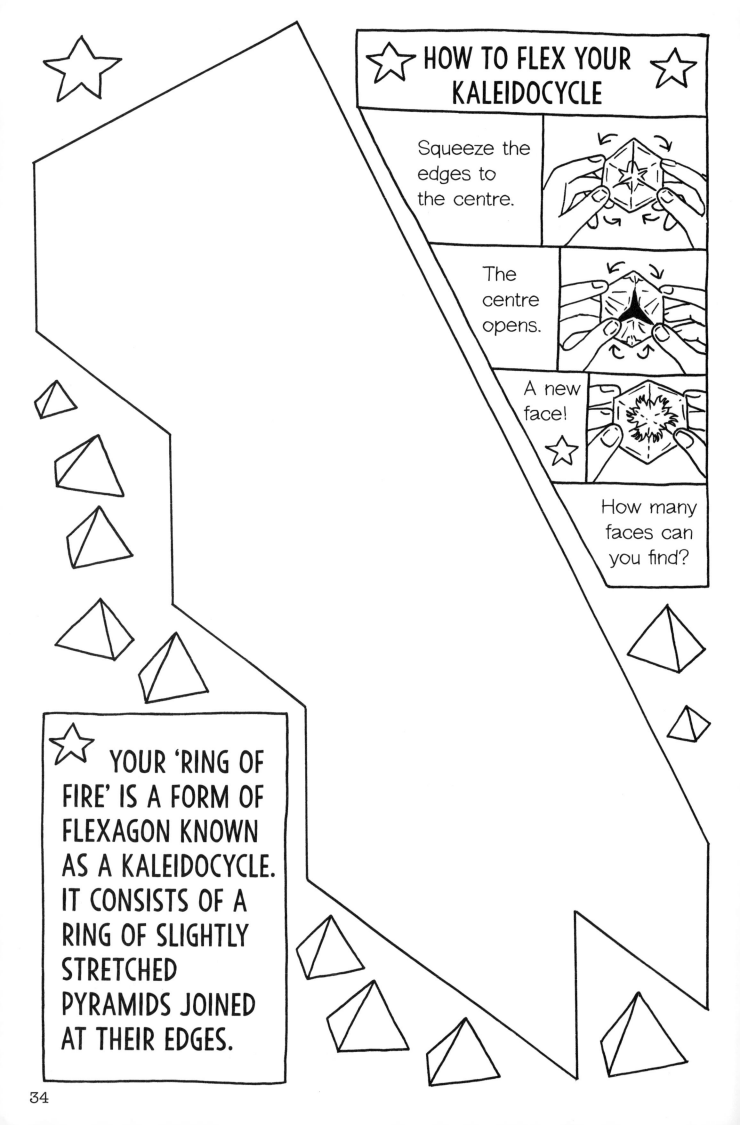

HOW TO FLEX YOUR KALEIDOCYCLE

Squeeze the edges to the centre.

The centre opens.

A new face!

How many faces can you find?

YOUR 'RING OF FIRE' IS A FORM OF FLEXAGON KNOWN AS A KALEIDOCYCLE. IT CONSISTS OF A RING OF SLIGHTLY STRETCHED PYRAMIDS JOINED AT THEIR EDGES.

RIDDLE OF THE REP-TILES

'Rep-tiles' is the name given to polygons that can be combined to make larger versions of themselves.

First, cut out all the tiles. Next, can you combine the four small pictures of Cleopatra to make the larger shape? And how about the four small sphinxes?

COLOUR THE PIECES

MORE

WHAT'S THE MATHS?

The name 'rep-tile' ('replicating tile') was coined by US mathematician Solomon Golomb (1932 – 2016).

Many regular and irregular polygons will replicate their shape, just like the pieces here.

Can you see how to rep-tile four pieces all this shape?

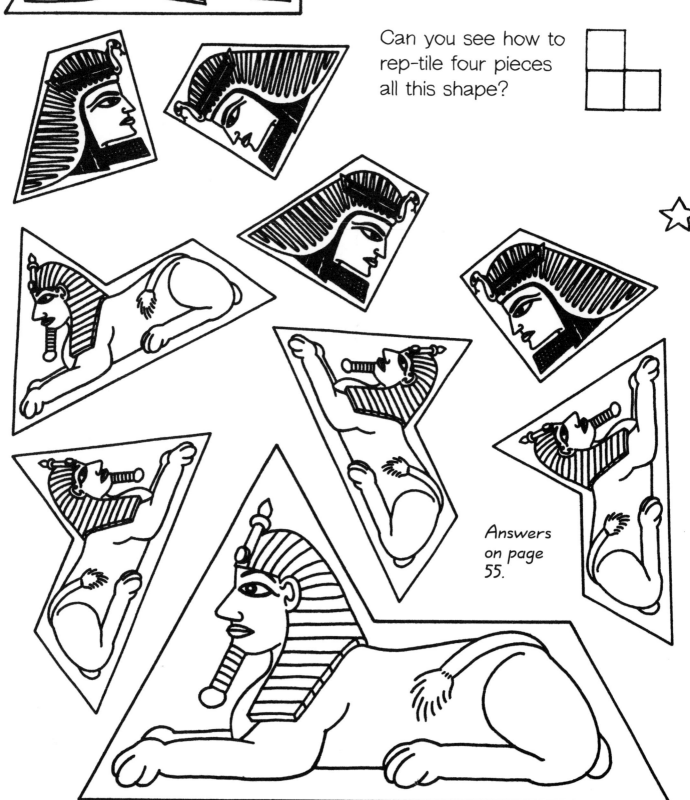

Answers on page 55.

HATS OFF!

RE-STACK THE HATS IN AS FEW MOVES AS POSSIBLE!

Colour, cut-out and make up the four maths hats and the rug below. Next, stack the hats on the 'A' in reverse order of size, smallest on top. The challenge is to re-stack the hats in the same order from 'A' to 'B' by moving a single hat one or two spaces at a time, left or right. However, you must never place a larger hat on top of a smaller one.

HOW FEW MOVES WILL YOU NEED?

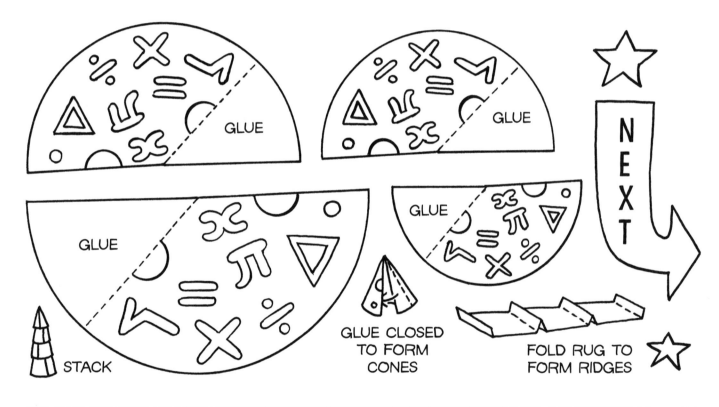

GLUE

GLUE

GLUE

GLUE

STACK

GLUE CLOSED TO FORM CONES

NEXT

FOLD RUG TO FORM RIDGES

A   2   B

WHAT'S THE MATHS?

See page 56 for the fewest moves needed.

This game is a version of a famous maths puzzle known as 'The Tower of Hanoi'. However, it has nothing to do with any actual towers or Hanoi, the capital city of Vietnam. In fact, the game was invented by French mathematician Edouard Lucas in 1883.

The lowest number of moves needed to solve the puzzle is given by a simple mathematical formula based on the number of hats involved. A stack of ten hats would require over 1,000 moves!

EDOUARD LUCAS

(1842 – 1891)

The formula for the least moves needed is $2^n - 1$.

Try the game with a stack of **5** or more coins.

THE POWER OF PYTHAGORAS

 This page can read your mind using the 'Power of Pythagoras'. Place seven coins on the mystic runes so that no two or more coins are in the same row or same column. Next, add up the seven numbers under the coins. Concentrate hard on the head of Pythagoras, then turn to page 56. Wow!

CONCENTRATE!

CONCENTRATE!

21	27	17	14	19	29	20
9	15	5	2	7	17	8
13	19	9	6	11	21	12
11	17	7	4	9	19	10
10	16	6	3	8	18	9
18	24	14	11	16	26	17
19	25	15	12	17	27	18

20TH JULY 1969

"ONE GIANT LEAP FOR MANKIND"

Katherine Johnson is an African-American maths whizz who worked on the calculations for the Apollo 11 space flight, the first mission to land people on the Moon.

Born in West Virginia, USA, in 1918, the young Katherine loved numbers so much that she counted everything – including all the knives, forks and plates when she did the washing up.

YOUNG KATHERINE

APOLLO COMMAND MODULE

Katherine was one of several African-American women who carried out important maths for the USA space programme (NASA). Originally they went uncredited because of their gender and their skin colour, but now they have been honoured and made the subject of a hit Hollywood film.

HIDDEN FIGURES

 Can you count all the forks in the pages of this book, including this one?

Answer on page 56.

Colour the pieces then press them out and assemble as shown below.

GLUE

GLUE TO HEAD ON REVERSE SIDE

NECK PIECE (CURL)

GLUE TO E

GLUE

APOLLO 11 FLIGHT PLAN

1 GLUE FOLD INTO TRIANGLE

2 ADD ARMS

3 NOD!

SATURN V ROCKET

GLUE TO INSIDE BASE

KATHERINE JOHNSON

E

KATHERINE JOHNSON

African-American mathematician/ astrophysicist

Born: USA, 26th August 1918

FAB FACT: At NASA, Katherine was called a "human computer".

GLUE
TO
HEAD

Katherine was
awarded the
'Presidential Medal
of Freedom'.

The medal is
the highest US
civilian honour.

☆ HOMEWORK GURU ☆

☆ This twenty-faced shape can help you with your homework.

☆ Colour, press out and fold along all the creases, then glue each tab under its adjacent face.

☆ Fill in the blanks with your own ideas.

MAKE A SHAPE THAT TELLS YOU WHAT TO DO.

"Eat pizza" Yay!

☆ **DONE!**

TAPE CAN HELP

GLUE

GLUE

GLUE

Stick at it!

Grab a snack

You choose

GLUE

Check the fridge

Just chill

Do it later

GLUE

Get some air

Roll again

Just do it!

Carry on

GLUE

GLUE

Ten minutes more

Check your phone

Grab some tunes

GLUE

Full steam ahead

Eat pizza

Walk the dog

Watch TV

GLUE

GLUE   GLUE

HOW TO USE YOUR GURU

1 Do some homework.

2 Roll your Guru.

3 Act on what it tells you.

WHAT'S THE MATHS? ☆➤

43

VERTICES
(CORNERS)

FACE

EDGE

Your homework guru is a regular solid known to mathematicians as an icosahedron ('eye-co-sa-hee-dron'). It has twenty faces, each one an equilateral triangle, and is the fifth and last of the Platonic solids.

Goodbye!

HOW MANY EDGES? HOW MANY VERTICES?	See page 56

Non-Platonic solids have a mixture of faces - not all of them are the same size and shape.

The panels of some soccer balls are a mixture of pentagons and hexagons.

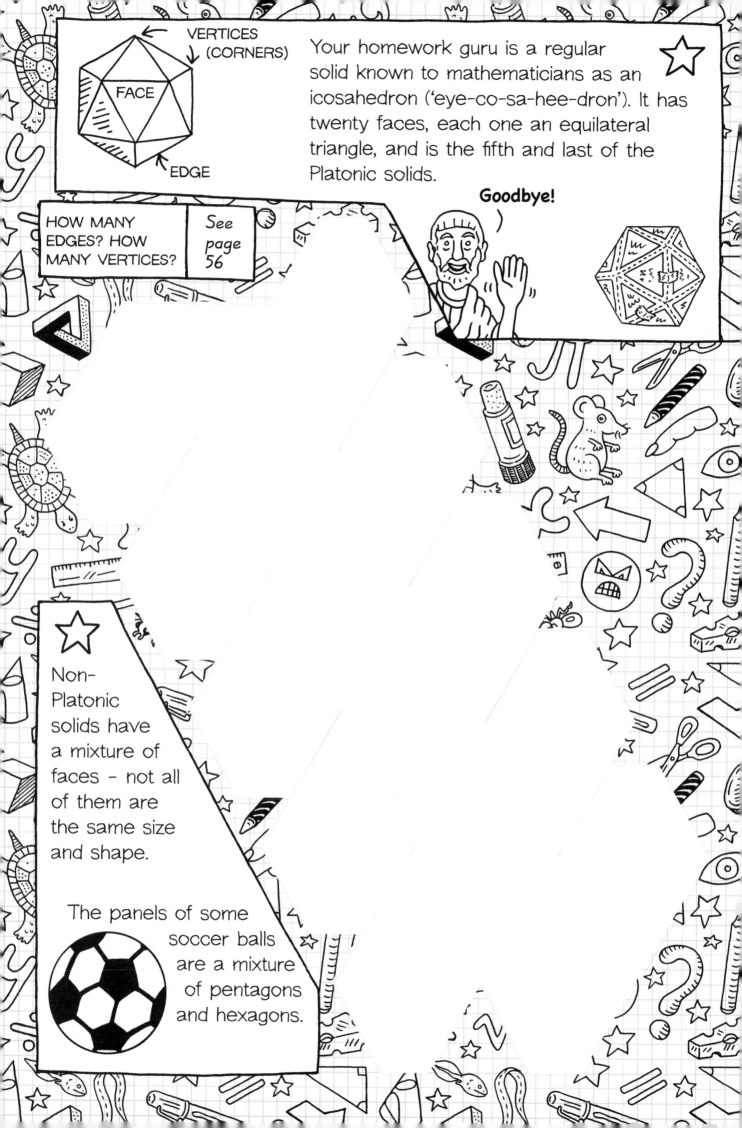

PHARAOH'S STORY

CAN YOU SOLVE THIS ANCIENT MYSTERY?

 Colour and press out the three identically-shaped pieces and fold and glue them as below.

FOLD AND GLUE SHUT.

 DONE!

Each piece forms an irregular, square-based pyramid.

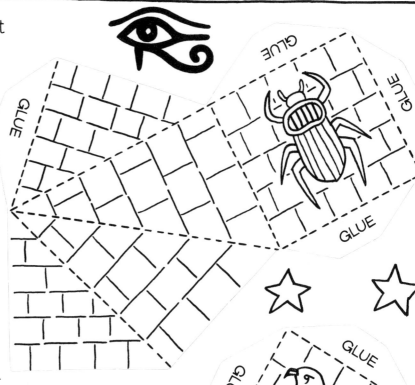

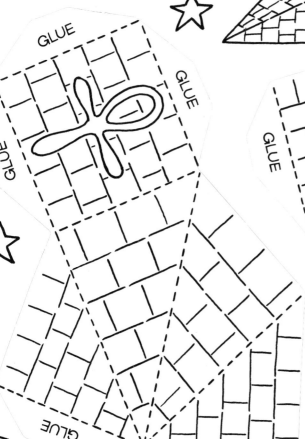

 NEXT!

45

CAN YOU PIECE TOGETHER THIS ANCIENT PUZZLE?

1 There was once a pharaoh who tried to build a cheap pyramid – in just three parts.

2 But when the pieces were put together they only produced three-quarters of a full pyramid.

MAKE THIS SHAPE

3 "That's no good!" cried the pharaoh, but suddenly he realized he could combine the same three pieces to make a different tomb with another regular shape.

CAN YOU?

⭐ If you need a clue, the pharaoh changed his name to 'Squaraoh'.

Answer on page 56.

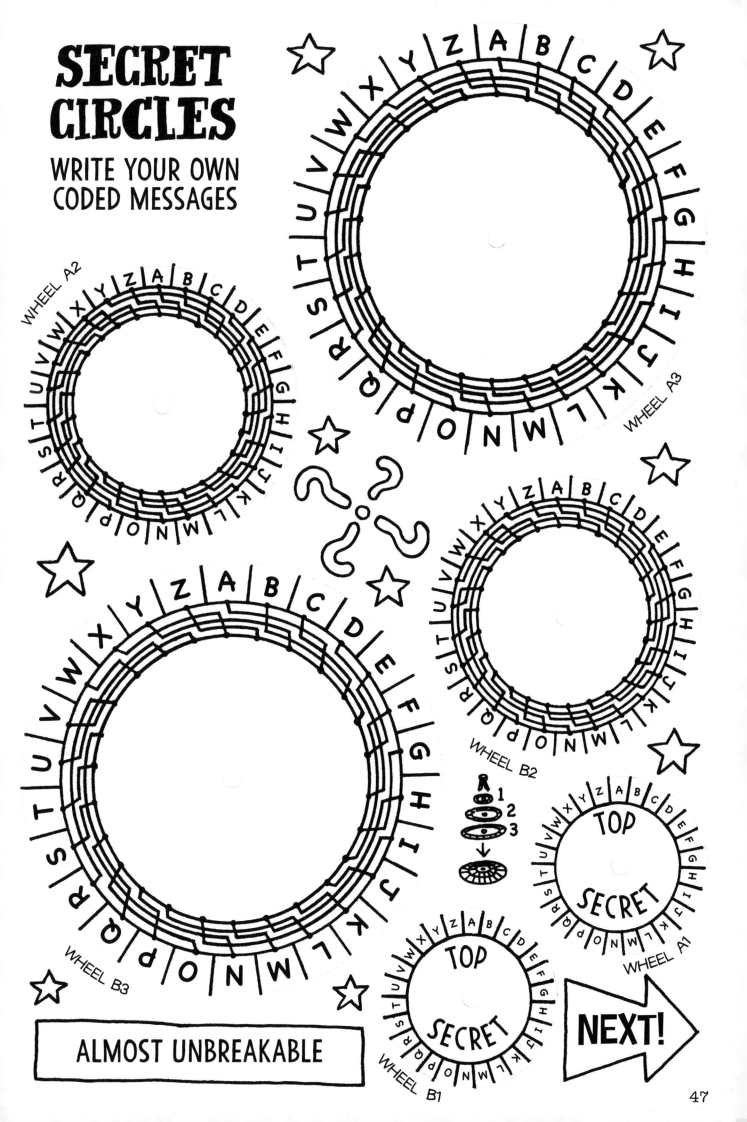

SECRET CIRCLES

WRITE YOUR OWN CODED MESSAGES

WHEEL A2

WHEEL A3

WHEEL B2

WHEEL A1

TOP SECRET

WHEEL B3

ALMOST UNBREAKABLE

TOP SECRET

WHEEL B1

NEXT!

47

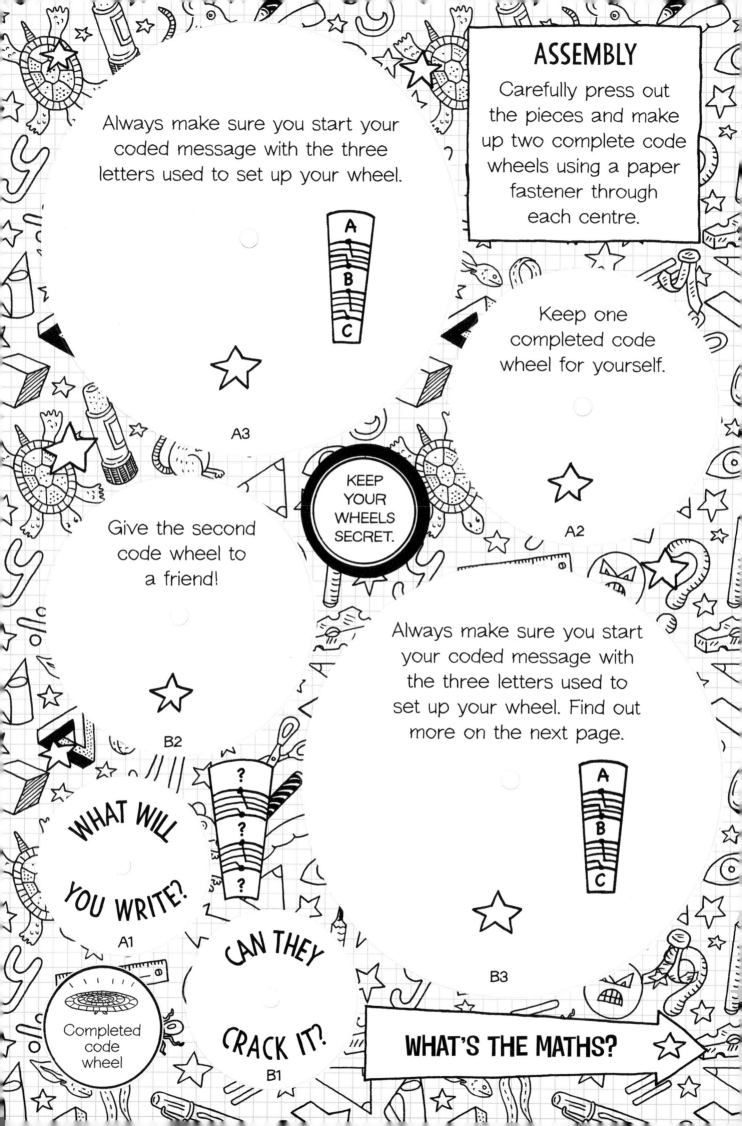

Always make sure you start your coded message with the three letters used to set up your wheel.

A3

ASSEMBLY

Carefully press out the pieces and make up two complete code wheels using a paper fastener through each centre.

Keep one completed code wheel for yourself.

A2

KEEP YOUR WHEELS SECRET.

Give the second code wheel to a friend!

B2

Always make sure you start your coded message with the three letters used to set up your wheel. Find out more on the next page.

B3

WHAT WILL YOU WRITE?

A1

Completed code wheel

CAN THEY CRACK IT?

B1

WHAT'S THE MATHS?

Cryptology is the study of codes and ciphers. It is an important field in mathematics.

During World War Two, the Nazis used special 'Enigma' coding machines to encrypt their military communications.

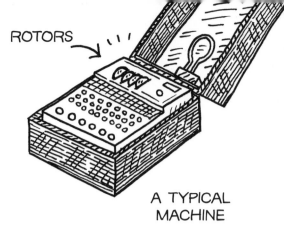
ROTORS

A TYPICAL MACHINE

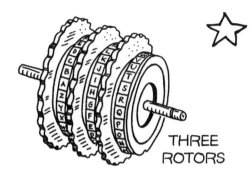
THREE ROTORS

 These machines had special rotors with the alphabet on them that swapped one letter for another many times to produce a scrambled message that could be deciphered with a machine set up exactly the same way.

 British maths genius Alan Turing led a secret team of code-breakers ("Ultra") that finally managed to crack the codes, shortening the war and saving lives.

ALAN TURING

Your code wheels are a simple form of the 'Enigma' rotors. To code a message, choose three letters vertically and line them up.
Here we have chosen **X**, **Y** and **Z**. You must start from the big wheel and work inwards to the smallest wheel. Always write your three letters at the start of any message you send e.g. '**XYZ**'.
Now, to encrypt the word '**CODE**', for example, simply follow the path of lines for each letter.

C to **F** to **K**; **O** to **S** to **X**; **D** to **H** to **L**; **E** to **I** to **N**.

So, you send the message: '**XYZKXLN**' ('**CODE**').

To decode, start from the small wheel and work outwards. Your friend can then set their wheels and decipher the words backwards.

CAN YOU DECODE THIS? '**DTBEKTPHCU**'? (See page 56.)

BRAIN STRAINERS

Mathematicians love a puzzle. Grab a pencil and see how swiftly you can solve these! *Answers on page 56.*

Pencils at the ready!

Good luck!

STAR TURN

Join all nine stars with just four straight lines while keeping your pencil on the page.

STICK TO IT

Draw these shapes without crossing a line or lifting off your pencil.

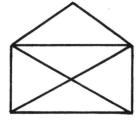
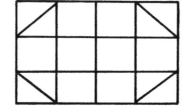
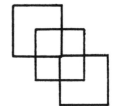
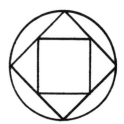

1 + 5 + 3 = 153

Use the same number three times to make this sum correct.

Divide the dial into four pieces, each adding up to the same numerical total.

Connect the matching shapes with three lines that do not cross.

MATHS ON THE MOON

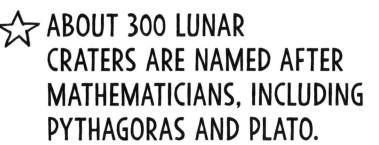

☆ ABOUT 300 LUNAR CRATERS ARE NAMED AFTER MATHEMATICIANS, INCLUDING PYTHAGORAS AND PLATO.

☆ Carefully cut out the moon below and you can fold it to produce a 'lunar ellipse'.

☆ Fold the Moon repeatedly so that every arrow on the edge of the far side overleaf touches the 'Plato' crater. Crease firmly, open it out, and do this for all 36 arrows.

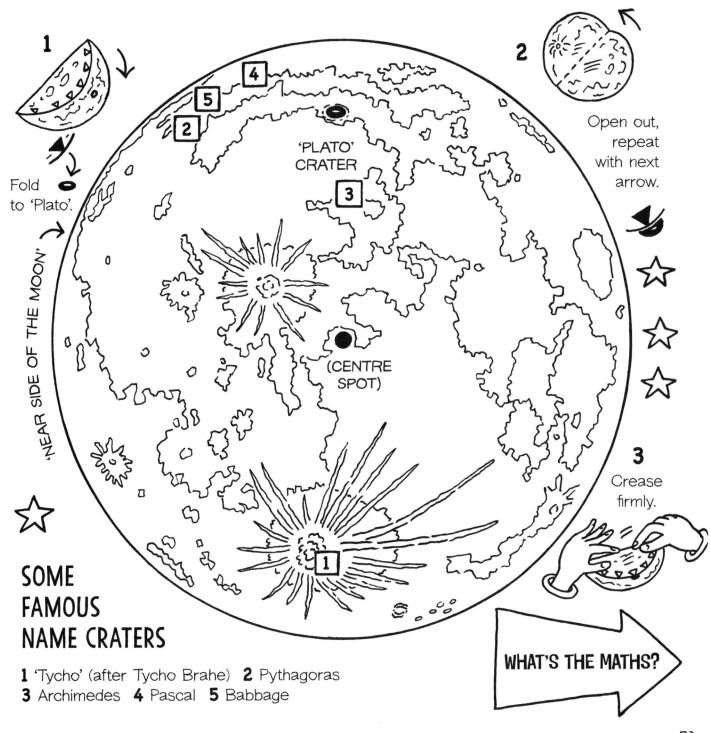

1

Fold to 'Plato'.

'NEAR SIDE OF THE MOON'

'PLATO' CRATER

4

5

2

3

(CENTRE SPOT)

1

2

Open out, repeat with next arrow.

☆

☆

☆

3

Crease firmly.

SOME FAMOUS NAME CRATERS

1 'Tycho' (after Tycho Brahe) **2** Pythagoras
3 Archimedes **4** Pascal **5** Babbage

WHAT'S THE MATHS?

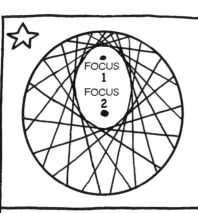

The 36 crease lines should enclose a regular curved space called an 'ellipse'. Every ellipse has two 'foci' ('foh-sy', which is the plural of 'focus'). A circle is a special form of an ellipse where the foci coincide.

For your lunar ellipse, the two foci are the crater 'Pluto' and the centre spot.

An ellipse, like a parabola (page 17), is another shape you can make by slicing across a cone.

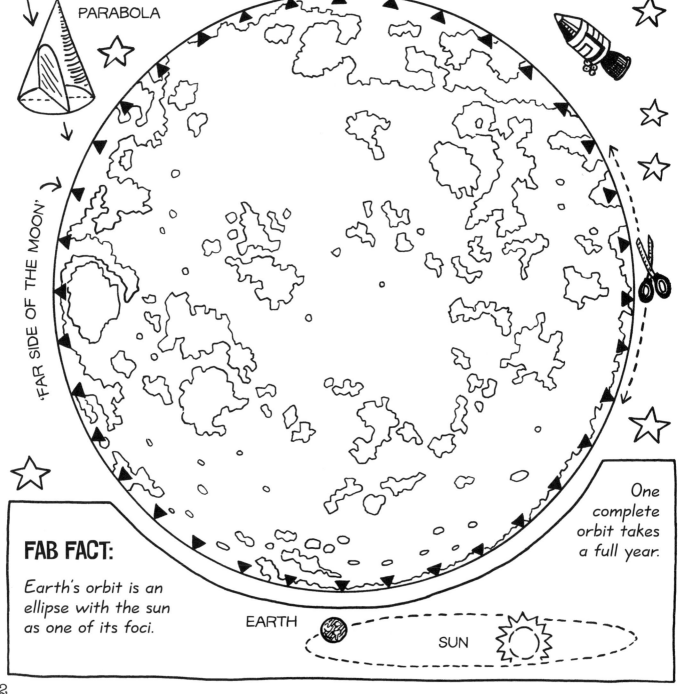

PARABOLA

'FAR SIDE OF THE MOON'

One complete orbit takes a full year.

FAB FACT:

Earth's orbit is an ellipse with the sun as one of its foci.

EARTH

SUN

ALL ANTS ON DECK

★ ★ MAKE YOUR OWN ★ ★
MARVELLOUS
MÖBIUS STRIP

The ants opposite have a long walk ahead of them. Make up their special walkway according to the instructions below and you will see why.

1 Carefully cut out both double-sided strips.

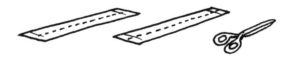

2 Glue the strips together to complete arrow '**A**'.

3 Next, put a half-twist into the extended strip and glue to complete arrow '**B**'.

GLUE

DONE!

NOW TURN THE PAGE

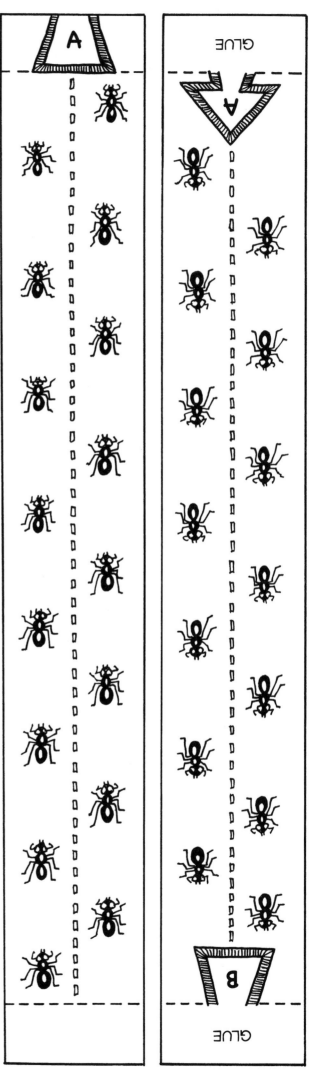

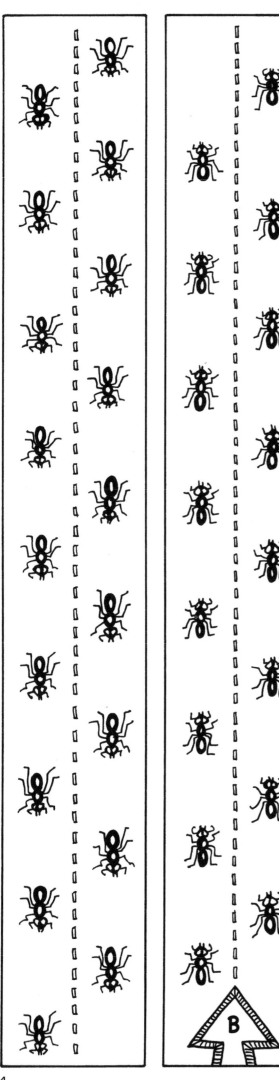

☆ The ants are marooned forever on a mathematical oddity known as a Möbius Strip.

REGULAR BAND	MÖBIUS STRIP/ANT BAND
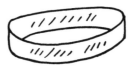	
Two surfaces, two edges	Just one surface, just one edge

Follow the ants on their journey with your finger and you will see that it goes inside, then outside, and back to the start. Amazingly it has only one surface.

AUGUST MÖBIUS
(1790 - 1868)

☆ **THE STRIP IS NAMED AFTER ITS 1858 INVENTOR, GERMAN MATHEMATICIAN AUGUST FERDINAND MÖBIUS.**

Next, cut your ant band down the dotted middle line using scissors. Can you guess what happens?

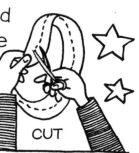

CUT

MAKE MORE MÖBIUS STRIPS FROM LENGTHS OF NEWSPAPER. ADD EXTRA TWISTS AND TRY CUTTING THOSE DOWN THE MIDDLE TOO. PREPARE TO BE AMAZED.

54

TRY NOT TO PEEK AT THE ANSWERS IN ADVANCE!

p7

A = circle; **B** = isosceles triangle;
C = square; **D** = rectangle; **E** = trapezoid;
F = crescent; **G** = rhombus;
H = equilateral triangle; **I** = kite;
J = parallelogram; **K** = pentagon;
L = scalene triangle (all sides and angles different); **M** = hexagon; **N** = decagon.

p11

The hieroglyph numerals add up to **1,111,222**.

p14

Join the pieces through the holes using paper fasteners and you can swing the triangle into the square and back again.

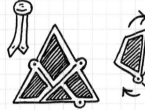

p16

The false net is '**K**'.

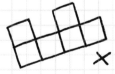 ✗

p19

The magic number is **15**.
The lines in the three magic squares add up to **15**, **34** and **65** respectively. The completed squares look like this:

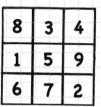

8	3	4
1	5	9
6	7	2

1	14	8	11
15	4	10	5
12	7	13	2
6	9	3	16

9	2	25	18	11
3	21	19	12	10
22	20	13	6	4
16	14	7	5	23
15	8	1	24	17

Can you devise your own **6 x 6** magic square? (The lines should add up to **111**.)

p23

Several possible solutions exist. Here's one:

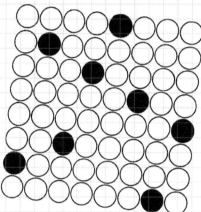

Can you find the two identical Face Invaders?

p32

Start with the faces where only one number is missing. Each face will total **65** and the three numbers on every vertex will all be the same.

p36

You need to flip some pieces to rep-tile the shapes.

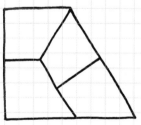

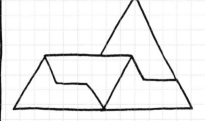 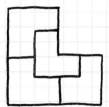

p37

The least possible moves for the four hats is $2^4 - 1 = 15$.
For five coins, it is **31**.
For six coins, it is **63**.

p39

The seven runes should always add up to **101**. This is because the grid is an 'addition square' – it was created from the sums of **14** numbers that have been removed from around its edge and added up to **101**. Placing the coins chooses seven pairs of 'invisible' numbers.

**8 + 14 + 4 + 1 + 6 + 16 + 7
+ 13 + 1 + 5 + 3 + 2 + 10 + 11 = 101**

	8	14	4	1	6	16	7
13	21	27	17	14	19	29	20
1	9	15	5	2	7	17	8
5	13	19	9	6	11	21	12
3	11	17	7	4	9	19	10
2	10	16	6	3	8	18	9
10	18	24	14	11	16	26	17
11	19	25	15	12	17	27	18

Can you spot '**101**' on the page? It's a hidden clue!

p40

There are 18 forks scattered throughout the book.

p44

30 edges (**E**), 12 vertices (**V**), 20 faces (**F**).
Does $F + V - E = 2$?

p46

The three pieces will form a cube.

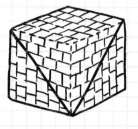

p49

The coded message is 'Yes I can'.

p50

This puzzle is said to have inspired the phrase, 'thinking outside the box', as the lines have to go 'outside the box' for you to solve it.

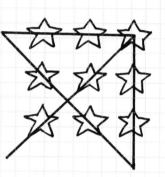

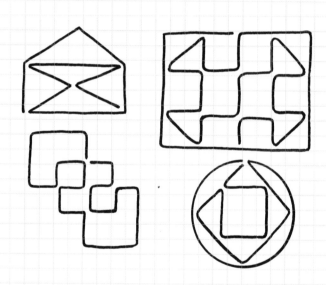

You add '**3**' three times, cubing the numbers
$1^3 + 5^3 + 3^3 = 153$
$(1) + (125) + (27) = 153$

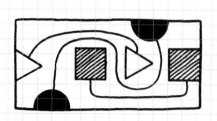

56